PATTERN PARTNERS

Look at each pair of partners in the left column. Can you find the item in one of the columns, A, B, or C, that will pair with the pattern in the center?

A   **B**   **C**

1.

2.

3.

4.

5.

6.

7.

8.

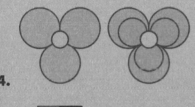

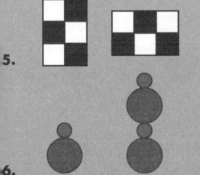

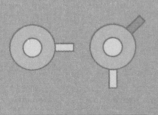

FORE!

Patty and her pals played a round of miniature golf. Now it's time to figure out who won.

Patty: 3
Paula: 4
Pete: 2
Perry: 6

Patty: 6
Paula: 1
Pete: 5
Perry: 2

Patty: 4
Paula: 2
Pete: 3
Perry: 1

Patty: 5
Paula: 3
Pete: 6
Perry: 4

Patty: 1
Paula: 6
Pete: 4
Perry: 5

Patty: 1
Paula: 6
Pete: 5
Perry: 1

Patty: 2
Paula: 5
Pete: 1
Perry: 3

Can you add up the scores of each golfer to find the champion?

Patty: 1
Paula: 2
Pete: 4
Perry: 5

Patty: 6
Paula: 1
Pete: 3
Perry: 3

Patty: 2
Paula: 4
Pete: 1
Perry: 5

Patty: 2
Paula: 3
Pete: 2
Perry: 1

Patty: 5
Paula: 5
Pete: 3
Perry: 4

Patty: 3
Paula: 4
Pete: 1
Perry: 2

Patty: 4
Paula: 1
Pete: 5
Perry: 3

Patty: 3
Paula: 5
Pete: 6
Perry: 4

Patty: 4
Paula: 1
Pete: 2
Perry: 3

Patty: 4
Paula: 3
Pete: 4
Perry: 2

Patty: 5
Paula: 2
Pete: 2
Perry: 6

FINISH

Hint on page 46

Illustration: R. Michael Palan

RING TOSS

Hint on page 46

Moses and Moesha each tossed three rings. Moses' rings landed on the 15, 40, and 45. Moesha's rings ended up on three numbers that were all different from one another and were not the same as Moses' numbers. Her score was $\frac{3}{4}$ of his. Which three numbers did Moesha ring up?

Illustration: Jerry Zimm

55 30 15 25 40

59 18 45 51 48 20

33 23 31 50 80

Answer on page 48

FOR THE TREES

Hint on page 46

Hilda the horticulturist wants to plant five new trees in order of height. Use the clues on the delivery sheet to list the trees in order from tallest to shortest.

Illustration: Rick Geary

The red oak is 72 inches tall.

The maple is 3 inches shorter than the cherry.

The birch is the shortest at 48 inches.

The cherry is 6 inches shorter than the tallest tree.

The spruce is 12 inches taller than the birch.

POTTER'S PLANTS

Answer on page 48

MOBILE MATH

Roy G. Biv is about to put his mobiles on display in the Mathmania Museum. Roy's number mobiles are balanced

by the value of the numbers that are hung on them. You can help open this exhibit by filling in the rest of the numbers.

For example, one mobile looks like this:

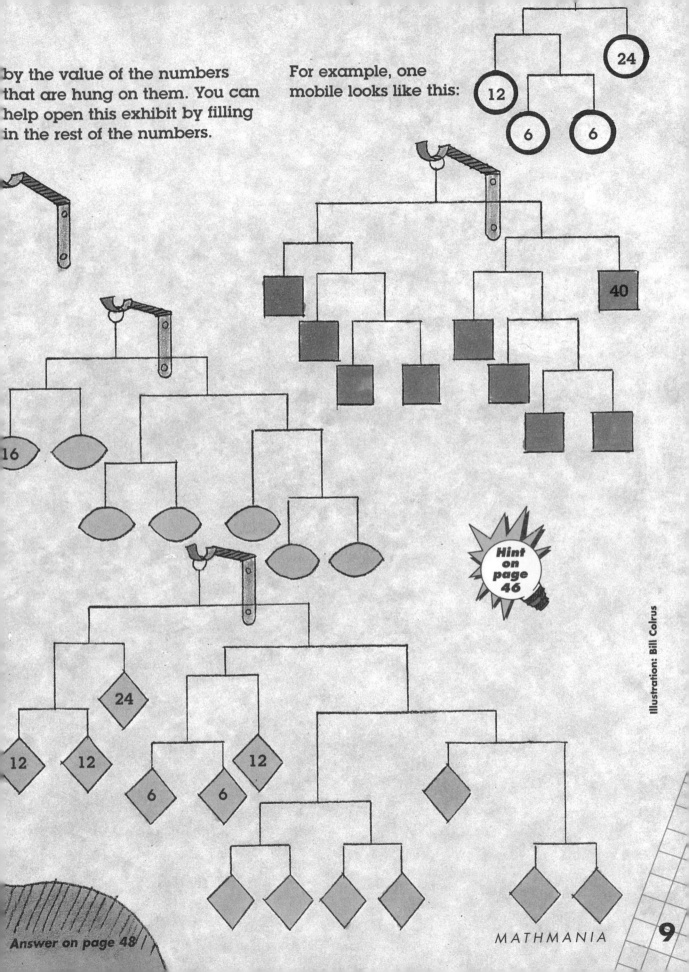

Hint on page 46

Answer on page 48

BLOPPERS

These are Bloppers.

These are not Bloppers.

Can you tell which of these creatures are Bloppers?

A

B

C

D

E

F

G

H

I

J

K

Answer on page 48

DOTS A LOT

Solve each problem in order as it appears on the list. Draw lines connecting the answers in order to create something on the fly.

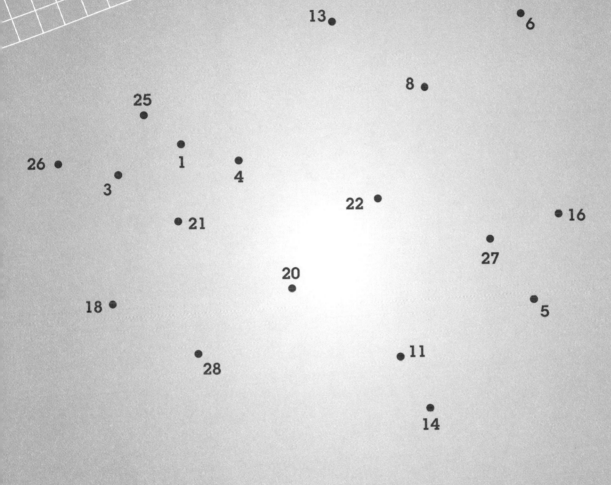

2 X 5 to 30 − 2 to 10 + 10 to 21 − 10 to 7 + 7 to 15 ÷ 3 to 8 X 2 to

3 X 9 to 11 + 11 to 16 ÷ 2 to 2 X 3 to 18 − 6 to 21 − 8 to 4 X 1

to 1 X 1 to 5 X 5 to 24 + 2 to 15 ÷ 5 to 3 X 7 to 3 X 6 to 5 + 5

Answer on page 48

SHELL GAME

of shells a point value.
Can you add up the points
and figure out who won?

= 1
= 15
= 5
= 20
= 10
= 25

Illustration: Doug Cushman

SCALE NEW HEIGHTS

Each number under the blanks below will finish the sequence for one ladder. Climb each ladder to find the sequence of the numbers between the rungs. Write your answer in the space between the top rungs. When you're finished, write the letter at the bottom of each ladder in the blank above the number that completed the sequence for that ladder.

8
6
4
2
T

1

23
11
5
2
U

2

8
4
2
1
P

3

12
9
6
3
E

4

4
3
2
1
S

5

2

P

Illustration: Rick Geary

Answer on page 48

Why did the carpenter like making ladders?

They were a ___ ___ ___ ___   ___ ___ from his last job.
           5 10 15 16   47 81

FAMOUS NAME

If you connect the dots in the order listed, you will find the name of the person described in this autobiography.

I was born in Poland and later moved to France. I became a well-known scientist and won the Nobel Prize twice in my lifetime—once for physics and once for chemistry. Together with my husband, Pierre, I discovered the element radium.

```
        A B C D E F G H I J
    1   · · · · · · · · · ·
    2   · · · · · · · · · ·
    3   · · · · · · · · · ·
    4   · · · · · · · · · ·
    5   · · · · · · · · · ·
    6   · · · · · · · · · ·
```

A1-A3	C1-C3	D1-D3	E1-E3	F1-F3	G1-G2	H1-H3
I1-I3	A4-A6	C4-C6	D4-D6	E4-E6	F4-F5	G4-G6
H4-H6	A1-B2	D1-E1	F1-G1	I1-J1	A6-B6	C6-D6
H6-I6	D2-E2	F2-G2	I2-J2	E5-F5	H5-I5	B2-C1
F2-G3	E5-F6	I3-J3	A4-B4	E4-F4	H4-I4	

Answer on page 49

ROLLING RIVERS

Get set to get wet! The lengths of 25 of the world's great rivers are waiting in this grid. First solve the problems to get the lengths. Then find the lengths across, up, down,

RIVER (continent)	LENGTH (in miles)	
Nile (Africa)	3000 + 1160	_____
Amazon (South America)	2000 × 2	_____
Yangtze (Asia)	800 × 4	_____
Congo (Africa)	2800 – 82	_____
Mackenzie (North America)	2000 + 635	_____
Mekong (Asia)	5200 ÷ 2	_____
Niger (Africa)	1295 × 2	_____
Mississippi (North America)	4680 ÷ 2	_____
Missouri (North America)	1500 + 815	_____
Volga (Asia)	1100 + 1190	_____
Yukon (North America)	2000 – 21	_____
Rio Grande (North America)	950 + 950	_____
Indus (Asia)	3600 ÷ 2	_____
Danube (Europe)	2000 – 224	_____
Euphrates (Africa)	825 + 875	_____
Ganges (Asia)	1700 – 140	_____
Colorado (North America)	725 + 725	_____
Irrawaddy (Asia)	1500 – 163	_____
Snake (North America)	950 + 88	_____
Ohio (North America)	1000 – 19	_____
Pecos (North America)	400 + 526	_____
Rhine (Europe)	405 + 415	_____
Po (Europe)	200 + 205	_____
Thames (Europe)	186 + 50	_____
Shannon (Europe)	23 × 10	_____

diagonally, or backward in the grid. Circle each number as you find it. Some digits may appear in more than one answer, and not every digit will be used.

```
1 1 4 0 2 3 6 1
7 4 9 3 6 2 4 7
7 2 1 0 2 5 9 0
6 5 3 4 0 3 1 0
9 4 7 4 1 6 0 8
7 4 9 3 0 2 2 1
9 8 4 4 3 0 4 4
1 2 7 1 8 1 0 4
```

Hint on page 46

Answer on page 49

17

LIBRARY LAUGHS

Dewey has some funny books in his library. To check one out, solve each problem. Then go to the shelves to find the volume with the number that matches each answer. Put the matching letter in the blank beside each answer. Read down the letters you've filled in to find the title and author of the book Dewey just finished reading.

Shelf 1: U 21, N 14, V 22, W 23

Shelf 2: F 6, J 10, K 11, E 5, B 2, R 18, D 4, A 1, T 20, Q 17, C 3, S 19, P 16

Shelf 3: L 12, X 24, Y 25, I 9, H 8, M 13

Shelf 4: Z 26, O 15, G 7

Illustration: Scott Peck

$17 - 4 =$ ___ ___

$3 \times 3 =$ ___ ___

$3 + 4 =$ ___ ___

$32 \div 4 =$ ___ ___

$5 \times 4 =$ ___ ___

$20 + 5 =$ ___ ___

$26 \div 2 =$ ___ ___

$15 + 6 =$ ___ ___

$25 - 6 =$ ___ ___

$24 \div 8 =$ ___ ___

$6 \times 2 =$ ___ ___

$2 + 3 =$ ___ ___

$17 + 2 =$ ___ ___

$8 - 6 =$ ___ ___

$5 \times 5 =$ ___ ___

$38 \div 2 =$ ___ ___

$19 - 18 =$ ___ ___

$6 + 7 =$ ___ ___

$22 - 3 =$ ___ ___

$3 \times 7 =$ ___ ___

$7 \times 2 =$ ___ ___

$9 + 5 =$ ___ ___

Hint on page 46

Answer on page 49

RIGHT OUT

Hint on page 46

Can you help Sir Cumnavigate find the correct path out of this problem? From where he stands, he must draw 11 straight lines that are connected until he reaches the exit. However, the king has declared that Sir C. must use only right-hand turns and must enter every square at least once. Luckily, lines may cross one another.

EXIT

DIGIT
DOES IT

Inspector Digit likes to go to the movies after a hard day of detection. But who can enjoy a film without popcorn? When the lights went down

someone passed this note to
the Inspector. Now he's on the
case and hopes to reel in
whoever ruined his film.

NOW PLAYING
THE
THING

‾ ‾ ‾ ‾   ‾ ‾ ‾ ‾ ‾ ‾ ‾ ‾ ‾ ‾   ‾ ‾ ‾ ‾ ‾,
2 11 5 20   14 9 16 17 11 3 18 1 20   2 14 8 14 18

‾ ‾ ‾ ‾ ‾   ‾ ‾   ‾ ‾ ‾   ‾ ‾'   ‾ ‾ ‾
16 1 20 20 21 18 1   17 1 17   14 9   4 7 18

‾ ‾ ‾ ‾ ‾ ‾ ‾   ‾ ‾ ‾ ‾   ‾ ‾ ‾
16 1 12 11 1 9 11   12 5 2 11   1 10 10

‾ ‾ ‾ ‾   ‾ ‾ ‾   ‾ ‾ ‾   ‾ ‾ ‾ ‾ ‾ ‾.
19 14 18 6   5 15 15   18 6 11   17 1 17 3 1 20 9

‾ ‾   ‾ ‾ ‾   ‾ ‾ ‾ ‾   ‾ ‾ ‾ ‾
14 10   21 1 7   10 14 9 2   13 7 16 18

‾ ‾,   ‾ ‾ ‾ ‾ ‾ ‾   ‾ ‾   ‾ ‾'
O A   17 14 11 3 11 16   1 10   14 18

‾ ‾ ‾ ‾ ‾   ‾ ‾,   ‾ ‾ ‾   ‾ ‾   ‾ ‾ ‾
21 1 7 15 15   4 11   6 1 18   1 9   18 6 11

‾ ‾ ‾ ‾ ‾.   ‾ ‾   ‾ ‾ ‾   ‾ ‾ ‾ ‾ ‾ ‾ ‾ ‾ ‾ ‾
18 20 5 14 15   14 12   9 1 18   4 7 18 18 11 20 14 9 8

‾ ‾ ‾   ‾ ‾'   ‾ ‾ ‾   ‾ ‾   ‾ ‾ ‾ ‾ ‾
21 1 7   7 17   4 7 18   14   9 11 11 2

‾ ‾ ‾ ‾   ‾ ‾ ‾ ‾ ‾!
21 1 7 20   6 11 15 17

‾ ‾ ‾   ‾ ‾ ‾ ‾ ‾ ‾ ‾
18 6 11   3 1 15 1 9 11 15

Hint
on
page
46

Illustration: Joe Boddy

CANDY
POPS
YUMS

SCRAMBLED PICTURE

Copy these mixed-up rectangles onto the next page to unscramble the scene. The letters and

A-3 A-1 A-4 A-2

B-2 B-4 B-3 B-1

C-4 C-2 C-1 C-3

D-3 D-1 D-4 D-2

numbers tell you where each
rectangle belongs. We've done
the first one, A-3, to start you off.

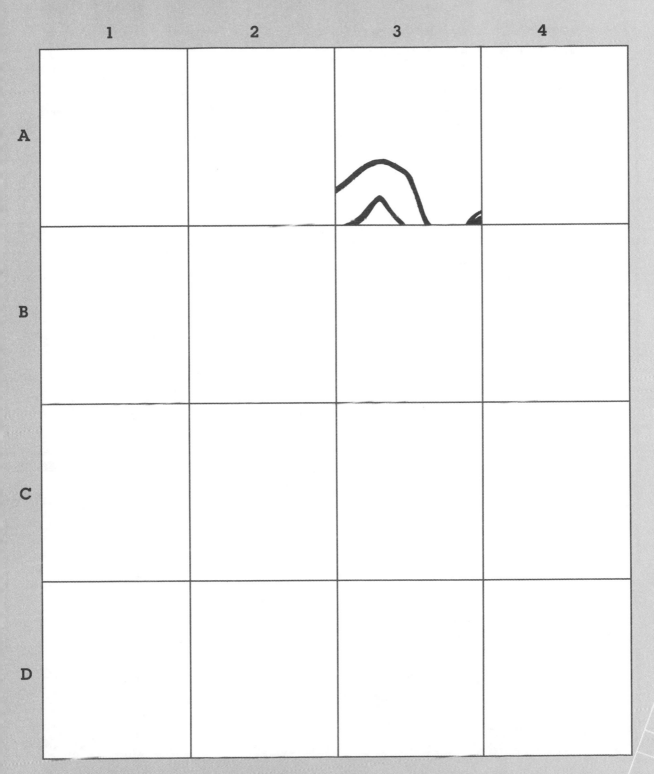

	1	2	3	4
A				
B				
C				
D				

Answer on page 49

STACKING STANLEY

Stan is building a pyramid of boxes. The bottom level of his pyramid, shown here measures 6 boxes by 6 boxes. How many levels will he need to build his pyramid? How many boxes will he use in all to complete the pyramid?

ACME

Hint on page 46

Answer on page 50

GET COORDINATED

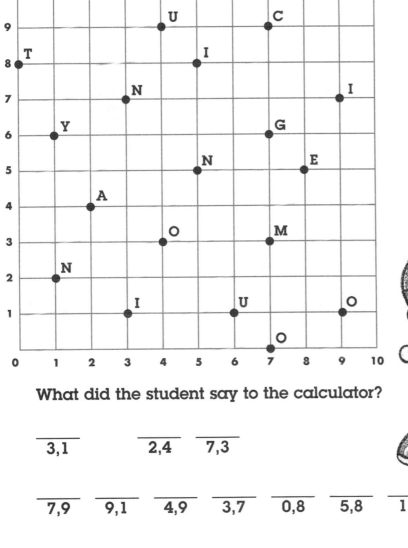

To find the answer to this riddle, fill in each blank with a letter from the grid. To find the right letter, look at the numbers beneath each blank. The numbers match a coordinate on the grid. The first number tells you how many lines to count across the bottom, while the second number tells you how many rows to count up. For example, the numbers under the first blank tell you to go across 3 and then up 1 to the *I*.

What did the student say to the calculator?

$$\overline{\hspace{1cm}}_{3,1} \quad\quad \overline{\hspace{1cm}}_{2,4} \ \overline{\hspace{1cm}}_{7,3}$$

$$\overline{\hspace{1cm}}_{7,9} \ \overline{\hspace{1cm}}_{9,1} \ \overline{\hspace{1cm}}_{4,9} \ \overline{\hspace{1cm}}_{3,7} \ \overline{\hspace{1cm}}_{0,8} \ \overline{\hspace{1cm}}_{5,8} \ \overline{\hspace{1cm}}_{1,2} \ \overline{\hspace{1cm}}_{7,6}$$

$$\overline{\hspace{1cm}}_{4,3} \ \overline{\hspace{1cm}}_{5,5} \quad\quad \overline{\hspace{1cm}}_{1,6} \ \overline{\hspace{1cm}}_{7,0} \ \overline{\hspace{1cm}}_{6,1}.$$

Answer on page 50

CIRCLE SENSE

Examples:

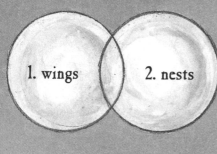

1. Animals that are wild.
2. Animals that are tame.
These two circles are separate because an animal can only be one or the other.

1. Animals that have wings.
2. Animals that have nests.
These two circles intersect because some animals have wings and also have nests. Those animals would go in the space where the circles overlap. Some animals would go only in the left circle because these animals have wings but do not have nests (like bats). Other animals would go in the right circle because these creatures live in nests but don't have wings (like squirrels).

Now look at the other lists below. Which set of graphs illustrates each list? Write the letter of the correct graph in the box beside the list. Watch the numbers to be sure you have the correct set of graphs.

1. Lead
2. Things that float
3. Things that are alive ☐

1. Black objects
2. Crows
3. Things that fly ☐

1. Books
2. Nonfiction
3. Fiction ☐

1. Roses
2. Red flowers
3. Flowers that bloom
   in summer ☐

1. Band members
2. Flute players
3. First-chair flutists ☐

1. Sweet drinks
2. Carbonated drinks
3. Beverages ☐

Illustration: Kit Wray

described in each case. Look at the example graphs, called Venn diagrams, first.

A 2. 3. 1.

B 1. 2. 3.

C 1. 2. 3.

D 3. 1. 2.

E 1. 2. 3.

F 1. 2. 3.

Hint on page 47

FILL IN THE BLANK

A number from 0 to 9 belongs in each box shown. Can you use the numbers we've provided as clues to help figure out where the missing numbers belong?

☐ × ☐ = 48

☐ × ☐ = 63

5 × ☐ ☐ = ☐ 0

☐ × ☐ = 1 ☐

Now try this set of problems.

100 ÷ ☐ = ☐ 5

☐ ☐ ÷ 5 = 6

☐ ☐ ÷ ☐ = 7

☐ ☐ ÷ ☐ = 13

Hint on page 47

Answer on page 50

WE WASH WINDOWS

Hint on page 47

Willis, Wallace, Wanda, and Wendy all wash windows. On Wednesday, they washed all 150 windows on Wilma's World of Wondrous Whistles. From the clues, can you tell how many windows each one washed?

1. Wendy, new to the job, washed only $\frac{1}{2}$ the number of windows Wallace washed.
2. The number of windows Willis washed equals Wanda's total plus $\frac{1}{4}$ of Wallace's.
3. Wallace washed $\frac{1}{3}$ of all the windows minus 2.
4. Wanda washed 15 fewer windows than Wallace.

Answer on page 50

CROSSNUMBER

Answer each question as you would in a regular crossword, and then place the numbers into the grid, one number per box.

ACROSS

1. In the calendar of months, March, June, and September arrive in this order.
4. 300 – 89
7. Number of years in 6 centuries
8. Number of years in $\frac{1}{2}$ of a millennium
9. 50,000 × 2
12. Sequence of numbers between 3 and 10
17. 35 minutes before 10 o'clock
18. The number to dial in an emergency
20. Bicentennial number
21. Number of minutes in $2\frac{1}{2}$ hours

DOWN

1. Inches in a yard
2. 1 minute after 6 o'clock
3. $\frac{9}{10}$ of 1000
4. 125 × 2
5. The roman numeral C stands for this number.
6. The prefix "milli" means this number.
10. Secret agent James Bond's number
11. Year Columbus first reached the New World
13. May twentieth, written numerically
14. 10% of 6500
15. 18 Across minus 20
16. September fifteenth, written numerically
19. The roman numeral X stands for this number.

Illustration: Rick Geary

Hint on page 47

Answer on page 50

LOOP-THE-LOOP

Every number can be looped together with one other number. The key to finding the pairs is to look for those numbers that have a difference of 9 when the smaller number is subtracted from the larger. Pairs can be looped across, up, down, backward, or diagonally. Each number will be looped with only one other number.

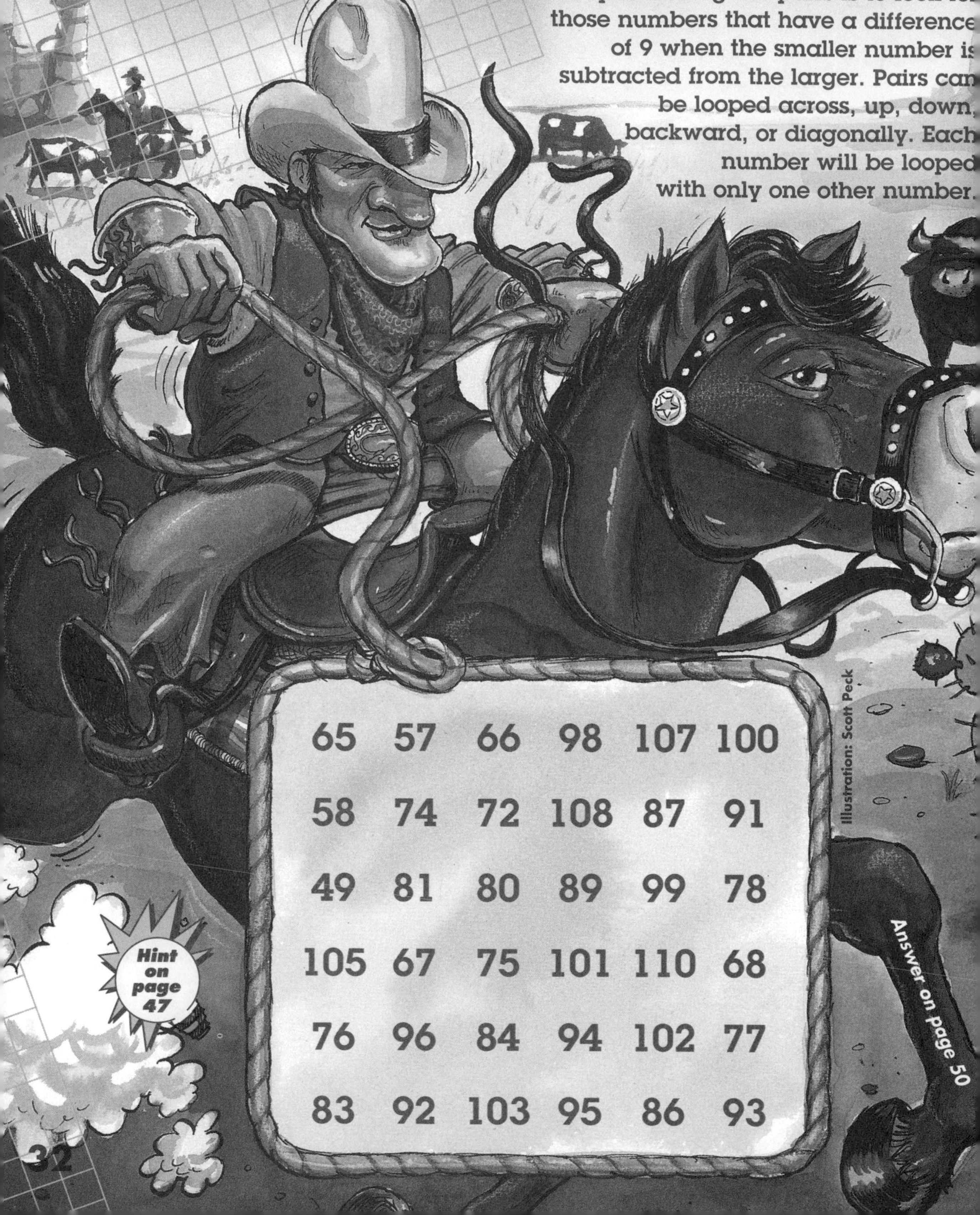

65	57	66	98	107	100
58	74	72	108	87	91
49	81	80	89	99	78
105	67	75	101	110	68
76	96	84	94	102	77
83	92	103	95	86	93

Hint on page 47

Answer on page 50

Illustration: Scott Peck

COLOR BY SHAPES

Use the key to color the shapes.

⚡ — Light Blue **X — Dark Blue**
● — Green **★ — White**
▲ — Pink **■ — Black**

Answer on page 50

KEEPING TRACK

Hint
on
page
47

*T*he winner of the Milk Drinkers 500 gets a gold trophy and a case of baked beans

1. Every car under normal circumstances took 2 minutes to finish each lap. There are 24 laps in all.

2. The car with four digits stopped for 18 minutes when its driver spotted a pileated woodpecker on a fence.

3. The driver of the car with the number that matches the days in a week is very superstitious. On lap 13, she refused to step on the gas in case something went wrong. Add 5 minutes while she glided.

4. The two cars with the numbers that could represent the months of July and November both went through car washes, which added 20 minutes to their times.

5. The pit crew for the negative-numbered car is the pits. Crew members took 12 minutes to change a tire because they were sharing a bowl of cherries.

6. All the drivers with even-numbered cars stopped to sing "Happy Birthday" to the announcer. Each added 2 minutes to his or her time.

From the clues, can you tell who won this wacky race? Who came in second, third, and so on?

. The driver of the car with the number that is 1 cent short of a dollar ran off the track and hasn't been seen since.

. The driver of the car 5 x 5 - 2 noticed an ice-cream cone shape in the clouds and pulled over to look. Add 45 minutes.

. Every car with a number greater than 20 has a driver who forgot to pay the gasoline tax and was penalized 10 minutes.

0. The driver of car 32 ÷ 2 had an allergy attack. She sneezed so hard, she pressed the gas pedal to the floor for laps 15 through 20. This shaved 8 minutes off her time.

1. The drivers of all the odd-numbered cars stopped to put on sunscreen during lap 12. Each added 3 minutes.

2. The driver with the car number that equals 18 + 17 ate banana-and-kiwi kebabs for breakfast. This gave him an extra energy boost and saved 6 minutes off his time.

Illustration: David Helton

Answer on page 50

TRIANGLE TWINS

Find the matching pairs of triangles. The triangles might be different sizes and face different directions, but they have the same angles and proportional sides.

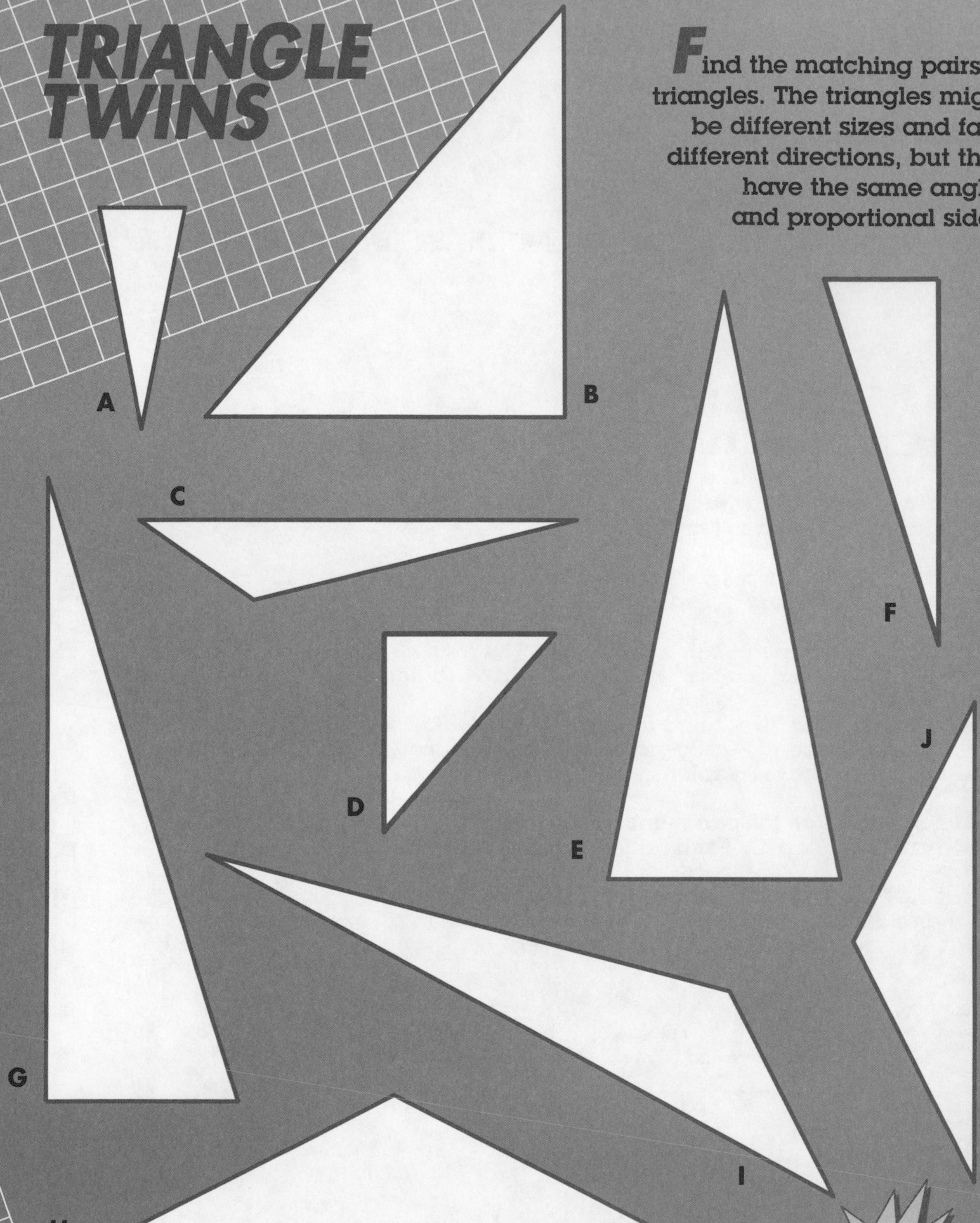

A

B

C

D

E

F

G

H

I

J

Hint on page 47

Answer on page 50

MEASURE POUR MEASURE

Hint on page 47

Can you think of a way to get the required amount of liquid in each case, using only the cups and pitchers given?

1. Get a measure of exactly 2 cups. When A is filled, it holds 5 cups.

3 cups
B

5 cups
A

2. Get a measure of exactly 3 cups. When A is filled, it holds 7 cups.

2 cups
B

7 cups
A

3. Get a measure of exactly 15 cups. When A is filled, it holds 9 cups.

2 cups
B

9 cups
A

REWIND TIME

Veronica is rewinding all the tapes that came in. If each 10 minutes of video takes 15 seconds to rewind,

Hint on page 47

170 minutes

Singing on the Train

BLUBBERING HEIGHTS

200 minutes

and she can only rewind one tape at a time, how long will it take her to finish the job?

2½ hours

Awesome Powers

Castle Blanca

It's a Wonderful Fife

100 minutes

1 hour, 50 minutes

STUART BIG

GIGANATOSAURUS

180 minutes

BUGBATS

210 minutes

DOCTOR DOMUCH

1½ hours

120 minutes

130 minutes

Answer on page 51

101 Chihuahuas

MATHMAGIC

Here's a way to astound a friend.

Write down a six-digit number, using any of the numbers from 1 to 9. At least three of the numbers must be different.

Mix up the digits to make a new number.

Subtract the smaller number from the larger one.

Add together the individual digits of this answer.

If there is more than one digit in this new answer, add together those individual digits.

Now we can reveal the answer. Check it out on page 51.

Illustration: Marc Nadel

PRECISE ICE

Can you draw this figure without crossing over or going back along any lines?

Illustration: Barbara Gray

Answer on page 51

41

BIRTHDAY HUNT

Holly can't remember where she hid her brother's birthday presents. You can help Holly recover the goods by finding

22 – 3	9 × 11	3 × 4	2 + 1
30 + 7	2 × 9	21 ÷ 3	70 – 7
6 – 3	3 + 7	43 – 4	16 + 4
7 × 5	16 – 6	5 – 4	2 + 3
17 – 6	2 + 9	36 ÷ 6	1 + 7
21 + 6	3 × 7	20 – 5	1 + 2
40 – 2	16 ÷ 2	2 + 4	20 ÷ 5
30 – 1	15 × 2	25 ÷ 5	10 ÷ 2
35 ÷ 7	6 + 3	3 × 11	9 + 1
2 × 2	4 + 6	10 – 3	6 – 5
11 – 8	1 + 4	7 × 9	6 + 6

START

42

the one path that has only
odd-numbered answers. She
can move across, up, down, or
backward, but not diagonally.

FINISH

4 × 5	3 × 9	8 + 9	2 × 10	17 − 12
50 ÷ 10	5 + 6	12 + 12	77 − 2	7 × 7
25 − 5	17 + 6	99 − 24	15 + 1	2 + 5
7 × 7	17 − 3	6 + 7	14 + 28	25 ÷ 5
63 ÷ 9	18 ÷ 3	77 − 12	5 × 9	15 × 3
16 − 5	7 + 9	2 × 7	2 × 11	100 ÷ 10
100 + 3	16 + 22	9 × 7	20 + 5	5 × 7
7 + 4	4 + 28	2 × 8	12 + 1	4 + 4
4 × 4	17 − 2	6 × 7	6 ÷ 2	42 ÷ 6
1 + 8	1 × 3	16 + 16	43 − 2	3 × 8
5 − 1	16 − 13	21 ÷ 7	16 + 5	18 + 3

Answer on page 51

MATHMANIA

SIMONE SAYS

Simone made the shape shown here. Now she wants to make three congruent squares by moving only four sticks. Can you show her how to do it?

Hint on page 47

Illustration: R. Michael Palan

Answer on page 51

SQUARE NUMBERS

The words for the numbers from 0 to 10 can be spelled out by connecting letters in the boxes that touch one another either across, up, down, or diagonally. The numbers in all the combined boxes for each word must add up to the total given. Some letters will be used in more than one word.

1 F	2 S	3 I	4 X	5 I
6 I	7 E	8 G	9 N	10 N
11 V	12 U	13 H	14 T	15 E
16 F	17 O	18 R	19 E	20 V
21 T	22 W	23 N	24 S	25 Z

Number Word	Boxes	Total
——	__ + __ + __	9
——	__ + __ + __ + __	25
——	__ + __ + __ + __ + __	79
——	__ + __ + __	59
——	__ + __ + __ + __ + __	45
——	__ + __ + __ + __	79
——	__ + __ + __ + __	39
——	__ + __ + __ + __ + __	88
——	__ + __ + __	60
——	__ + __ + __ + __	63
——	__ + __ + __	38

Hint on page 47

HINTS AND BRIGHT IDEAS

These hints may help with some of the trickier puzzles

COVER
Machine A adds 14 to each number going through it. Can you figure out what machine B does to change its numbers?

FORE! (pages 4-5)
Make a list of the 18 holes. Then add each golfer's scores for all 18 holes. The lowest score wins.

RING TOSS (page 6)
Moses scored 100 points. $\frac{3}{4}$ of 100 is 75.

FOR THE TREES (page 7)
The oak is the tallest tree.

MOBILE MATH (pages 8-9)
Numbers hung at the same level within each mobile have the same value.

ROLLING RIVERS (pages 16-17)
The rivers are listed in size order from longest to shortest.

LIBRARY LAUGHS (page 18)
Remember to consult the books to find the letter that matches each number.

RIGHT OUT (page 19)
Here are Sir C.'s first two moves:

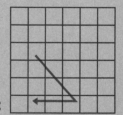

DIGIT DOES IT (pages 20-21)
The word *Inspector* appears in the note's greeting. Use the code numbers from this word to help figure out the rest of the message.

STACKING STANLEY (page 24)
Stan's next level will also be a square, with 5 boxes to a side.

CIRCLE SENSE (pages 26-27)
Pay attention to the numbers within each set of graphs. See how they match up with the lists.

FILL IN THE BLANK (page 28)
What does 5×10 equal?

WE WASH WINDOWS (page 29)
You know the total number is 150. $\frac{1}{3}$ of that is 50. $50 - 2 = 48$.

CROSSNUMBER (pages 30-31)
Roman numeral X stands for 10, and C stands for 100, which is also the number of years in a century. Divide 6500 by 10 to get 10%.

LOOP-THE-LOOP (page 32)
74 minus the 65 in the corner equals 9.

KEEPING TRACK (pages 34-35)
According to the first statement, a car normally takes 48 minutes to complete the race.

TRIANGLE TWINS (page 36)
A and E are similar.

MEASURE POUR MEASURE (page 37)
You can pour water into the pitcher, or pour it out altogether.

REWIND TIME (pages 38-39)
Convert each time into minutes. Divide the number of minutes by 10. Multiply that number by 15 seconds. Now you'll have the rewind time in seconds, which you can change to minutes.

SIMONE SAYS (page 44)
Congruent means shapes that are the same design and the same size.

SQUARE NUMBERS (page 45)
SIX is the first number on the list.
Boxes 2, 3, and 4 equal 9.

ANSWERS

COVER

A	B
2 + 14 = 16	2 × 3 + 1 = 7
5 + 14 = 19	5 × 3 + 1 = 16
3 + 14 = 17	3 × 3 + 1 = 10
8 + 14 = 22	8 × 3 + 1 = 25
7 + 14 = 21	7 × 3 + 1 = 22

PATTERN PARTNERS (page 3)

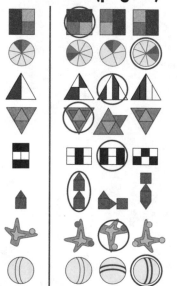

FORE! (pages 4-5)

Patty	Paula	Pete	Perry
61	58	59	60

Paula won.

RING TOSS (page 6)

Moses scored 100 points; $\frac{3}{4}$ of 100 is 75.
Moesha's rings landed on the 20, 25, and 30.

FOR THE TREES (page 7)

Red oak—72 inches
Cherry—66 inches
Maple—63 inches
Spruce—60 inches
Birch—48 inches

MOBILE MATH (pages 8-9)

BLOPPERS (page 10)

Bloppers A, E, and J have two dark interior lines and two antennae and contain a small triangle and a small square.

DOTS A LOT (page 11)

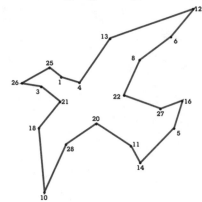

SHELL GAME (pages 12-13)

Sarah: 25 + 10 + 20 + 30 = 85
Sadie: 45 + 10 + 20 + 9 = 84
Sam: 5 + 20 + 10 + 30 + 10 = 75
Sarah won.

SCALE NEW HEIGHTS (page 14)

Ladder 1: 10 (count by even numbers)
Ladder 2: 47 (double the number before and add 1)
Ladder 3: 16 (double the number before)
Ladder 4: 15 (count by 3s)
Ladder 5: 5 (count by 1s)
Ladder 6: 81 (number before times 3)

Why did the carpenter like making ladders?
They were a STEP UP from his last job.

FAMOUS NAME (page 15)

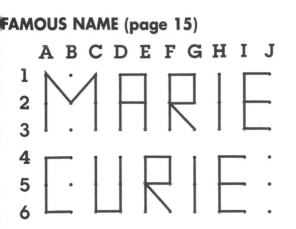

MARIE
CURIE

ROLLING RIVERS (pages 16-17)

RIVER	LENGTH (in miles)
Nile	$3000 + 1160 = 4160$
Amazon	$2000 \times 2 = 4000$
Yangtze	$800 \times 4 = 3200$
Congo	$2800 - 82 = 2718$
Mackenzie	$2000 + 635 = 2635$
Mekong	$5200 \div 2 = 2600$
Niger	$1295 \times 2 = 2590$
Mississippi	$4680 \div 2 = 2340$
Missouri	$1500 + 815 = 2315$
Volga	$1100 + 1190 = 2290$
Yukon	$2000 - 21 = 1979$
Rio Grande	$950 + 950 = 1900$
Indus	$3600 \div 2 = 1800$
Danube	$2000 - 224 = 1776$
Euphrates	$825 + 875 = 1700$
Ganges	$1700 - 140 = 1560$
Colorado	$725 + 725 = 1450$
Irrawaddy	$1500 - 163 = 1337$
Snake	$950 + 88 = 1038$
Ohio	$1000 - 19 = 981$
Pecos	$400 + 526 = 926$
Rhine	$405 + 415 = 820$
Po	$200 + 205 = 405$
Thames	$186 + 50 = 236$
Shannon	$23 \times 10 = 230$

LIBRARY LAUGHS (page 18)

$17 - 4 = 13$	M		$8 - 6 = 2$		B
$3 \times 3 = 9$	I		$5 \times 5 = 25$		Y
$3 + 4 = 7$	G		$38 \div 2 = 19$		S
$32 \div 4 = 8$	H		$19 - 18 = 1$		A
$5 \times 4 = 20$	T		$6 + 7 = 13$		M
$20 + 5 = 25$	Y		$22 - 3 = 19$		S
$26 \div 2 = 13$	M		$3 \times 7 = 21$		U
$15 + 6 = 21$	U		$7 \times 2 = 14$		N
$25 - 6 = 19$	S		$9 + 5 = 14$		N
$24 \div 8 = 3$	C				
$6 \times 2 = 12$	L				
$2 + 3 = 5$	E				
$17 + 2 = 19$	S				

MIGHTY MUSCLES
by Sam Sunn

RIGHT OUT (page 19)

DIGIT DOES IT (pages 20-21)

Dear Inspector Digit,
Sorry to pop in, but someone made off with all the popcorn. If you find just 15 pieces of it, you'll be hot on the trail. I'm not buttering you up, but I need your help!
The Colonel

a-5	f-10	l-15	r-20	y-21
b-4	g-8	m-12	s-16	
c-3	h-6	n-9	t-18	
d-2	i-14	o-1	u-7	
e-11	j-13	p-17	w-19	

SCRAMBLED PICTURE (pages 22-23)

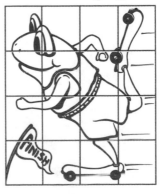

STACKING STANLEY (page 24)
Stan's pyramid will be 6 levels high. He will stack 91 boxes altogether.

GET COORDINATED (page 25)
What did the student say to the calculator? I AM COUNTING ON YOU.

CIRCLE SENSE (pages 26-27)

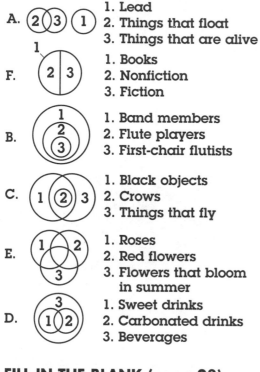

A.
1. Lead
2. Things that float
3. Things that are alive

F.
1. Books
2. Nonfiction
3. Fiction

B.
1. Band members
2. Flute players
3. First-chair flutists

C.
1. Black objects
2. Crows
3. Things that fly

E.
1. Roses
2. Red flowers
3. Flowers that bloom in summer

D.
1. Sweet drinks
2. Carbonated drinks
3. Beverages

FILL IN THE BLANK (page 28)
These are our answers. The order of your numbers may vary.

$8 \times 6 = 48$ $100 \div 4 = 25$
$9 \times 7 = 63$ $30 \div 5 = 6$
$5 \times 10 = 50$ $56 \div 8 = 7$
$4 \times 3 = 12$ $91 \div 7 = 13$

WE WASH WINDOWS (page 29)
Wallace washed 48 windows, Willis washed 45, Wanda washed 33, and Wendy washed 24.

CROSSNUMBER (pages 30-31)

LOOP-THE-LOOP (page 32)

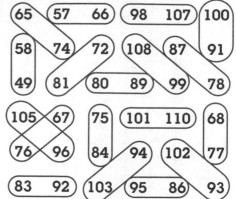

COLOR BY SHAPES (page 33)

KEEPING TRACK (pages 34-35)

PLACE	CAR	TIME
1st	16	42 minutes (48 + 2 – 8)
2nd	35	55 minutes (48 + 10 + 3 – 6)
3rd	72	60 minutes (48 + 2 + 10)
4th	-5	63 minutes (48 + 12 + 3)
5th	11	71 minutes (48 + 20 + 3)
6th	7	76 minutes (48 + 5 + 20 + 3)
7th	1896	78 minutes (48 + 18 + 2 + 10)
8th	23	106 minutes (48 + 45 + 10 + 3
9th	99	Never finished the race

TRIANGLE TWINS (page 36)
A—E, B—D, C—I, F—G, H—J

MEASURE POUR MEASURE (page 37)
Here are our answers. You may have found other ways to get the measures.
1. A is filled with 5 cups. Pour that into B until B is full. The amount left in A should be 2 cups.
2. A is filled with 7 cups. Pour 2 cups of water from A into B. Pour water from B into the pitcher. Fill B again from A. The amount left in A should be 3 cups.
3. A is filled with 9 cups. Pour all the water in the pitcher. Fill B three times and add that amount to the pitcher.